REBELLIOUS RHYMES

PERFECT FOR ALL KIDS' STORY TIMES

WRITTEN & ILLUSTRATED BY DANIEL HILLIARD

For my amazing wife and kids,
Vicky, Lola, Herbie and Elwood.
Love you all.

ISBN: 978-1-8383087-1-1

Published by Hilliard's Tall Tales in 2020

info@hilliardstalltales.com

www.hilliardstalltales.com

THIS BOOK BELONGS TO:

CONTENTS

Hi

McLARK

Mr McLark is a horrible chap
With fingers like worms and a nose like a tap.

He took his dog Bob for a walk in the park.
It was past six o'clock and suitably dark.

Bob crouched down behind a big bush.
He grunted and growled, then gave a huge push.

Out plopped a poo: it was slimy and brown
with such a foul stench you could smell it in town.

How could McLark leave this pile of dog poo
For someone to step in and mess up their shoe?

It wasn't Bob's
fault: McLark
was to blame.
But what made it
worse was this
poo had a brain!

A poo that
could walk,
even talk,
jump and run.
A piece of dog dirt
that was thinking
of fun.

And so off it
went, right down
the street.
One step at a time
with its little
poo feet.

It followed McLark
right back to his house
(to the untrained eye it looked like a mouse).

It spotted McLark asleep in his chair.
Three seconds later it jumped in his hair.

McLark woke up yelling – a terrible din.
Well, maybe next time he'll use a poo bin!

SWEET DREAMS

You'll never find monsters under your bed,
The zombies and vampires lurk in your head.

Big wolves and giants that eat kids in jelly –
That is just stuff you've seen on the telly.

So let go of your worries, and climb into bed,
Dream about nice things that happen instead.

Flying high in the sky, eating a flump,
Or hearing an old lady doing a trump.

Now you're tucked in: time to shut your eyes tight.
Remember I love you. Sweet dreams, goodnight.

FLUSHED

Joe loved his pet fish. Her name was Zed.
She was a joker, and thought she'd play dead.

She hung on the surface, perfectly still.
"Zed's had it," thought Joe, "She isn't just ill."

Joe knew in a flash what he needed to do.
He plucked the fish out and into the loo.

He yanked the loo handle and wished her goodbye –
Then at the last moment Zed opened her eye.

Too late! She was spinning round and round
And shot down the toilet with a gurgling sound.

She rushed through the pipes as fast as can be.
Next thing she knew, she was shot out to sea.

The water was salty, cold, deep and dark.
Zed swam round the corner and spotted a shark.

She hid by a bike and peered round a spoke
And wished she'd never played this practical joke.

STITCH

Jenny's mum and dad would not allow pets.
"We don't want expensive bills from the vets."

"A dog or a cat would be filthy and smelly
And for the same price we could have a new telly!"

So Jenny had a thought: could she make her own pet?
One that might smell a bit, but would not need a vet.

She went out and gathered some rancid roadkill.
Then stitched bits together – which gave her a thrill.

Its head was a badger, its body a cat.
Plus the legs of a dog and the tail of a rat.

She jumped on its chest with both of her feet,
Its heart was actually starting to beat.

Jenny named it Stitch on a walk to the beach.
He soon wriggled free, and shot off with a screech.

The next thing Stitch did was completely insane:
It swallowed a cat and shot down a drain.

Jenny followed him down. It was damp, foul and dark.
She could hear Stitch ahead by the sound of his bark.

8

Then Jenny slipped on some mucky green slime
And fell down the ladder two steps at a time.

The water smelled bad. It was murky and brown.
With no one to help she was sure she would drown.

But on her last breath, with seconds to spare,
Stitch pulled Jenny out by the scruff of her hair.

Jenny was amazed she'd made something so clever.
She knew right then, they'd be best friends forever.

POPCORN TERRY

Terry the silverback sits in his cage,
Everyone staring. It fills him with rage.

"I don't belong here. I'm as smart as can be."
So he reaches across and snaffles the key.

Later that night he opens his door.
The other zoo animals watch him in awe.

The lions stay quiet. The monkeys don't shout.
Terry the silverback is now breaking out!

He darts past the cages, as swift as a flea,
Hiding in shadows, so the guard doesn't see.

Up on the roof, across the town hall.
Back down a drainpipe, and straight up a wall.

So far so good – it's going as planned,
Then a satellite dish comes away in his hand.

He falls through a roof without being seen.
King Kong is playing on a huge movie screen.

The lady says, "Welcome." (She's there on her own)
"There's no charge today as you're 38 stone."

Terry sits at the back, watching with glee.
A bag of popcorn upon his right knee.

THE SHLOMBAT

What on earth is this fur-covered freak,
With big, bulging eyes and a sharp, pointed beak?

I'm told it's a Shlombat – a strange little beast
That giggles and squeaks as it flies from the East.

With wings like a bat it crosses the sea
And lands when it's tired to drink up spilt tea.

"So what does it do?" I hear you all say.
Well, it creeps round your house... but only in May.

Then, when it's dark, the Shlombat plays silly
Like tying up laces or flashing its willy.

It loves stealing undies, or hiding Dad's socks
Or wiping its bum on your mum's fancy frocks.

When June comes round it flies out the door,
'Til next year, in May, when it creeps back for more.

STICKY BRAINS

RIP

Billy thought he was cool and incredibly brave,
When he jumped up and down and danced on a grave.

Then something stirred deep in the earth,
It let out a groan like a dog giving birth.

Billy was scared – he turned round and fled,
Already convinced he'd woken the dead.

And he had! Out they crept, one at a time,
Stinking of poo and covered in slime.

With sunken white eyes and bones on show,
The zombies were out and ready to go.

Billy ran fast 'til his legs gave him pains,
The zombies all wanted his soft, sticky brains!

He got to his room, rolled under the bed,
The zombies were after the stuff in his head!

A banging downstairs – they've got in the house!
Billy stays quiet, and still as a mouse.

A big pair of feet are crossing the floor.
He vows he will change and be naughty no more.

Dragged out of hiding, he opens his eyes,
But the person he sees is a massive surprise.

It's Dad after all. Billy cuddles him tight.
"Get back in bed, son. I'll leave on the light."

MMMM CANDY!

Rick lived in a sweet shop, which wasn't that great,
Because of the sweets that he wolfed down and ate.

Even on the loo he continued to eat,
Any old thing that was sticky and sweet.

Lollipops, chocolate and sherbert dip
When he bent down he'd always let rip.

Bigger and bigger he grew day by day.
"The greediest on earth," I heard people say.

And still he ate hotdogs, nuggets and wings
And loads more greasy, fattening things!

Even just walking he'd pant and he'd puff.
At last he decided enough was enough.

He went for a run. He wobbled like jelly!
Within a month he'd shrunk his huge belly.

Now all he eats is salad and brussels
To nourish his six-pack and huge bulging muscles.

He realises now eating junk was so silly,
For the first time in years he can see his own...

GRANDAD'S MAP

Grandad's stories were crazy and weird,
Like the time that he found a bird in his beard.

Lucy would sit and listen with pleasure,
Especially the one about lost buried treasure.

He took from his pocket a tatty old note
On which (it was rumoured) a pirate once wrote.

"It's a map of our yard with an X in the middle,
Just near the spot where our dog does a piddle."

Out we both went to dig up the gold.
I wore a hat so my head wasn't cold.

We soon found the spot in the dreary old yard,
I stuck in the spade and hit
something hard.

We peered in the hole –
what a shock and surprise!
We'd broken a pipe
and got sprayed in
the eyes.

BRIAN

It's really cool I live near a zoo,
I see penguins whilst on the loo.

I'd love a pet hippo, or a vampire bat,
But all we've got is a fat, ginger cat.

She spent the day in the lions' den
And didn't come home 'til after ten!

A few weeks passed and out popped a kitten.
From that day on I was completely smitten.

I'm really thrilled. I called him Brian
I soon realised he was a lion!

I arrive at school before the bell,
Eager to shock at show 'n' tell.

He really is an enormous size,
The children can't believe their eyes.

The teacher rocks up a second later,
Brian swallows her whole like an alligator.

DICK THE WIZARD

Most wizards do magic and live in great towers,
Yet Dick was a wizard of limited powers.

He was determined to mix an award winning spell,
But swallowed his lizard, and got very unwell.

He got worse overnight, and couldn't be nursed,
The cure was a spell he'd never rehearsed.

He mixed up the potion, in a big woman's shoe.
The duck's eyes and frog spit was starting to brew.

Dick stirred it up and gulped it all down
(He only spilled half on the front of his gown).

It didn't take long for the cocktail to work,
It made his whole body judder and jerk.

He howled like a gibbon and spun on the floor,
Banging his bonce on the open fridge door.

Dick really was rubbish at being a wizard,
The only result was he spewed up his lizard.

STRONG

Troy has the strength of a
hundred grown men.
Which is really unique
with him just being ten.

"How does he do it?"
I hear you all say.
Well, it happens at night,
not in the day!

You've heard of sleep
walking? This is like that.
Sleep press-ups and sit-ups
are what Troy is at.

He woke up one morning
to find his great gift.
There wasn't a weight
that he couldn't lift.

Elephants? Bulldozers?
Over his head!
And all from his workouts
while sleeping in bed.

GOLDEN RETRIEVER

Betty was our town's only tramp,
She sat in a doorway, cold and damp.

Hundreds of people passed every day.
They never said, "Hi." They just turned away.

No one cared why she was there,
All they did was point and stare.

At least she had her old dog, Pete,
Who spent his days warming her feet.

Pete didn't look well, he'd caught a cold,
The following night he coughed up some gold.

He barfed up more with every hour,
She had no clue Pete had this power.

Thanks to Pete, she's now proper flush,
Although her hair still looks like a bush.

Now when people see Betty they still point and stare.
Not for her barnet, but because she's the mayor.

THE PEEDLE MONSTER

We go swimming most weekends,
Diving, bombing, playing with friends.

Disaster strikes! I need to go!
I'll pee in here – no one will know.

I've heard the tales that pools have dye,
I'll find out now if that's a lie.

I let it out. What a relief!
I didn't know what lurked beneath!

He lies in wait where no one sees,
But he can smell when someone wees.

He's fat and pink – swims like a fish,
A face as big as a serving dish.

And what he does is very rude,
He steals your cozzie,
and leaves you nude.

So, next time you think
of peeing in a pool,
Use the toilet,
you mucky fool!

FISHY FLAPS

Sophie had flaps of skin near her ears,
The other kids teased – she'd end up in tears.

The bullies got worse as she grew bigger,
They'd call her four ears, with a laugh and a snigger.

Then came the day when the class learned to swim,
The bullies grabbed Sophie and chucked her right in!

The teacher rushed up, and cried, "I ain't taught 'er!"
But Sophie's ear flaps let her breathe underwater.

I WISH

Do you have a cat that brings home stuff that is dead?
A bird or a mouse, perhaps – missing a head?

Well, last week our Tom brought in something weird,
A tiny, wrinkly man with a long, scraggy beard.

I feared for the worst when he flopped on the drive,
Then he opened his eyes and exclaimed: "I'm alive!"

Quick as a flash he hid in my welly
(I think he felt glad he was not in Tom's belly.)

He drew a deep breath and started to speak
And told me about his terrible week.

"I'm a shaman by trade, and my name is Del.
I shrunk myself when I mucked up a spell.

I need two strange things to help me get big:
The slime of a fish and some hairs from a pig."

I gathered the stuff, whisked it up in a dish,
He said if it worked he'd grant me one wish.

With a fizz and some sparks he shot up like a rocket.
So I made my wish quick that he'd fit in my pocket.

CUSTARD POWER

I peer into my telescope
And stare at all the stars.
I wonder if the aliens
Are watching us from Mars.

I spot a little light
Out of the corner of my eye,
It shoots across the moon and then
It lights up all the sky.

It's not a star, it's not a plane –
It's flying way too low.
The only other explanation:
It's a UFO!

I'm down the stairs like superman.
My feet don't touch the floor,
I'm through the kitchen super-quick
And out the old back door.

Are my eyes playing tricks on me?
What is this I'm seeing?
Standing in our garden is
A tiny alien being.

He points towards his spaceship.
It's caked in grass and dirt.
He starts to dance and jig around
To show he isn't hurt.

He comes into the kitchen.
Could it be fuel he seeks?
I grab a tin of custard
That's been on a shelf for weeks.

He nods and smiles. We go outside.
I start to fill his ship,
I pour it very slowly,
Trying not to spill a drip.

He starts the engine up again.
(I think it's really cool.
No one will believe me
When I tell them all at school.)

The washing line spins round and round,
And flings off my mum's bras,
He shrinks down to a tiny dot
As he blasts back home to Mars.

MEAN MONROSE

Our class has a new teacher,
Her name is Miss Monrose.
Her face has beady eyes
And a crooked, pointed nose.

She skulks around the corridors
Looking to be mean.
She really is the scariest
that we have ever seen.

"Put this away! Put that away!
This thing does not live there!"
She barks her orders fiercely
As she combs her greasy hair.

If you're caught being silly,
Or acting very naughty,
She says she'll lock you in a box
Until you're nearly forty.

We hatch a plan to deal with her
And act without delay.
We all agree that none of us
Can stand another day.

The plan we have is simple:
We'll lure her in the box.
Once she's in, we'll slam the door
And hopefully it locks.

We know she really loves her cheese
(The smellier the better),
She always keeps a bite-sized chunk
Inside her stinky sweater.

We place the cheese inside the box
And wait for her to come.
It works! She's in! We slam the door!
It whacks her on the bum!

She screams and yells, then quietly says,
"I think I need a poo!"
That is going to have to wait.
She's off to Timbuktu.

THE CHATTERSLUG

We've just got back from our morning walk
Our dog Bert has learned to talk!

He swallowed a slug that he found on the beach
Ever since he's had the power of speech.

We stop in the kitchen. He looks in my eyes
He says in a gruff voice: "I love eating pies!"

We have a long chat about what he likes doing
(other than walking, weeing and pooing).

It turns out he wants to watch footie on telly
And hates his dog food as it upsets his belly.

Bert shivers and shudders. I ask, "What's the matter?"
He sicks up the slug that's been making him chatter!

It looks like a fat worm, all slimy and brown,
The cat pounces on it and gulps it right down.

The cat licks his lips and walks out the house
He says, "I'll be back with a fat, juicy mouse!"

THE DREADED DENTIST

I'm eight years old, my name is Badeer.
It's the dentist today – and that fills me with fear.

The shrill of the drill just puts me on edge,
I'd rather do homework, or eat all my veg.

Or let me be chased by a clown in the dark
Or swim in the sea and encounter a shark!

I'm scared he'll tell me my gums are all raw,
If only I'd cleaned my teeth more before!

I'd lie about brushing, I'd lick out the cap
Or just run my toothbrush under the tap.

"Now open up wide, little girl, if you would."
He has a good poke – and says, "Everything's good."

Oh, what a relief! I could run, skip and jump!
Or wheelie my bike right over a bump!

He gives me some fluid to spit in a tray
And a sticker that says: have a nice day!

I'll stop asking mum to buy sweets at the till
Or next time I might hear the sound of the drill...

THANKS FOR READING

DID YOU ENJOY THE RHYMES? IF YES, SPREAD THE WORD FAR AND WIDE BY TELLING YOUR FRIENDS AND FAMILY OR POST A NICE REVIEW ON SOCIAL MEDIA.

MY FIRST BOOK!!!

IF YOU ENJOYED THESE RHYMERS WHY NOT ORDER A COPY OF MY FIRST BOOK THE PICKERBEAST.

HILLIARD'S TALL TALES

www.hilliardstalltales.com

ACKNOWLEDGEMENTS

I'd like to thank my wife Vicky and good friend Rupe for helping me turn my initial blurb into coherent English. I'd also like to thank, Jonathan Manning, Simon Brown, Pat-a-cake, Jonners, Lottie, James Hazel and the rest of my family for their advice and encouragement along the way.

A BIT ABOUT THE AUTHOR

"Goodbye"

I'm a (happily) married 45 year old dad to three amazing children, Lola, Herbie and Elwood. I live in the beautiful town of Stamford, Lincolnshire. I've always had a gift for making up stories to entertain my kids, some of these went down so well, that I decided to write and illustrate some books. I created these alongside my day job as a graphic designer. So, here I am (too many) years later with the finished articles.

I hope you've enjoyed reading this book as much as I did creating it.

www.hilliardstalltales.com